ME WITHOUT YOU...

... IS LIKE SKY WITHOUT BLUE

LISA SWERLING AND RALPH LAZAR

summersdale

ME WITHOUT YOU

First published in 2011
This edition copyright © Lisa Swerling and Ralph Lazar 2016

Summersdale Publishers Ltd
46 West Street
Chichester
West Sussex
PO19 1RP
UK

www.summersdale.com

Printed and bound in China

ISBN: 978-1-84953-792-6

Substantial discounts on bulk quantities of Summersdale books are available to corporations, professional associations and other organisations. For details contact Nicky Douglas by telephone: +44 (0) 1243 756902, fax: +44 (0) 1243 786300 or email: nicky@summersdale.com.

TO ....

FROM ....

ME
WITHOUT
YOU

ME
WITHOUT
YOU
IS LIKE...

HAIR
WITHOUT
DO

RESTAURANT
WITHOUT
MENU

ESKIMO
WITHOUT
IGLOO

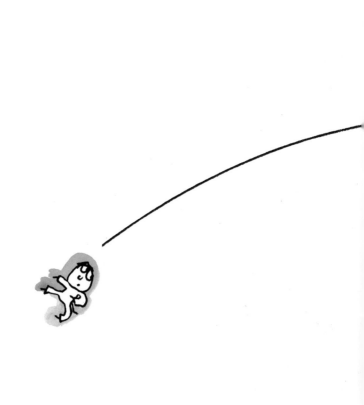

KUNG
WITHOUT
FU

BIKER
WITHOUT
TATTOO

GHOST
WITHOUT
BOO

MORNING

WITHOUT

DEW

COW
WITHOUT
MOO

DOVE
WITHOUT
COO

TANGO WITHOUT WITHOUT TWO

PARTY
WITHOUT
YAHOO!

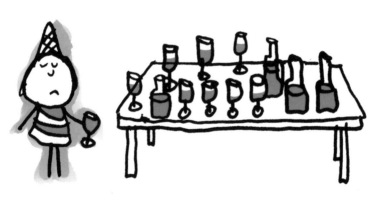

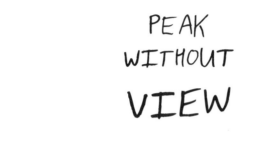

PEAK
WITHOUT
VIEW

MUCH
WITHOUT
ADO

HARRY
WITHOUT
YOU-KNOW-WHO

BORED
BORED
BORED

OAR
WITHOUT
CANOE

KANGA
WITHOUT
ROO

OCH AYE,
WITHOUT THE
NOO

OCH,
AYE

CHIMNEY
WITHOUT
FLUE

CLOCK WITHOUT CUCKOO

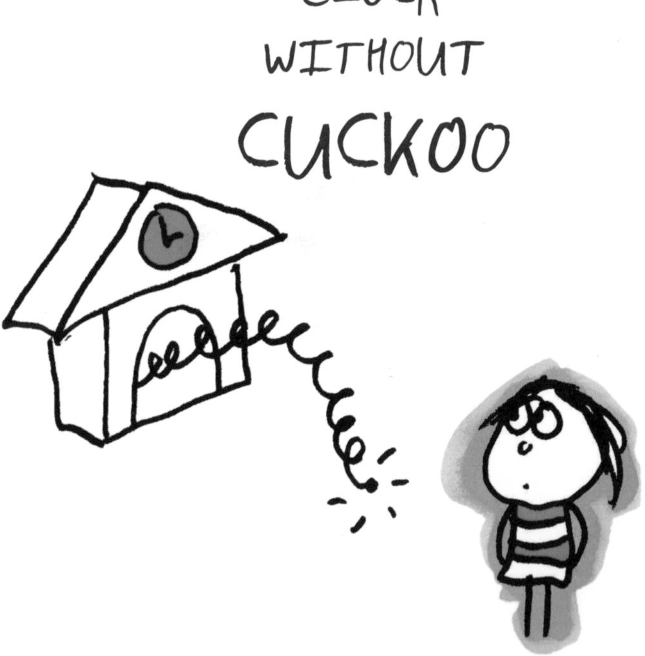

CAT
WITHOUT
MEW

IRISH
WITHOUT
STEW

FOOT
WITHOUT
SHOE

DETECTIVE WITHOUT A CLUE

WRECK
WITHOUT
RESCUE

SHOOBEE
WITHOUT
DOO

PENNY WITHOUT A CHEW

ZOO
WITHOUT
GNU

HOW
WITHOUT
DO-YOU-DO?

ANTIQUE
WITHOUT
VALUE

RAINBOW
WITHOUT
HUE

TEA
WITHOUT
BREW

PICNIC
WITHOUT
LOO

BELLS
WITHOUT
BLUE

COCK
WITHOUT
A-DOODLE-DO

SNOOKER WITHOUT A CUE

SHOW
WITHOUT
QUEUE

MOWGLI WITHOUT BALOO

A WITCH
WITHOUT HER
BREW

A COOK
WITHOUT HIS
SOUS

SNEEZE
WITHOUT A—

A—A—A——

TCHOO

DISCIPLE
WITHOUT
GURU

POTTY WITHOUT POO

COLD
FONDUE

PANDA
WITHOUT
BAMBOO

RUMBLE
RUMBLE

A PICTURE THAT'S ASKEW

A FLAT
KAZOO

A NON-SPICY
VINDALOO

A KNOT
I CAN'T

UNDO

BOO

HOO

HOO

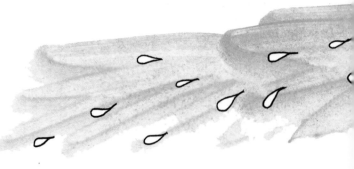

HOOOOOOOOOOooo

ME
WITHOUT
YOU!?

WHAT
WOULD I
DO?

BOO!

PHEW!

FOR EMMALINA

If you're interested in finding out more
about our books, find us on Facebook at
Summersdale Publishers and follow us on
Twitter at **@Summersdale**.

www.summersdale.com